This book belongs to

....

Hungry Floppy and Other Stories

How this collection works

This *Biff, Chip and Kipper* collection is one of a series of four books at **Read with Oxford Stage 3**. It is divided into two distinct halves.

The first half focuses on phonics, with two stories written in line with the phonics your child will have learned at school: *The Knight Who Was Afraid* and *Uncle Max*. The second half contains two stories that use everyday language: *Hungry Floppy* and *The Golden Touch*. These stories help to broaden your child's wider reading experience. There are also fun activities to enjoy throughout the book.

How to use this book

Find a time to read with your child when they are not too tired and are happy to concentrate for about fifteen minutes. Reading at this stage should be a shared and enjoyable experience. It is best to choose just one story for each session.

There are tips for each part of the book to help you make the most of the stories and activities. The tips for reading on pages 4 and 28 show you how to introduce your child to the phonics stories.

The tips for reading on pages 58 and 88 explain how you can best approach reading the stories that use a wider vocabulary. At the end of each of the four stories you will find four 'Talk about the story' questions. These will help your child to think about what they have read, and to relate the story to their own experiences. The questions are followed by a fun activity.

Enjoy sharing the stories!

Contents

OXFORD
UNIVERSITY PRESS

Phonics

Tips for reading *The Knight Who Was Afraid*

Children learn best when reading is relaxed and enjoyable.

- Talk about the title and the picture on page 5, and read the speech bubble.
- Identify the letter pattern *kn* in the title and the letter patterns *kn, n, wr* and *r* in the story, and talk about the sound they make when you read them ('n' as in *not*, and 'r' as in *ran*).
- Look at the words on page 6. Say the sound, then read the words (e.g. *kn – knight, n – name, wr – wraps, r – ran*).
- Read the story together, then find the words with *kn, n, wr* and *r* in them.
- Talk about the story and do the fun activities at the end of the story.

Children enjoy re-reading stories and this helps to build their confidence.

Have fun!

After you have read the story, find the ten rats in the pictures.

The main sounds practised in this story are 'kn' as in *knight* and 'r' as in *ran*.

For more activities, free eBooks and practical advice to help your child progress with reading visit **oxfordowl.co.uk**

The Knight Who Was Afraid

What was the knight afraid of?

Say the sounds and read the words

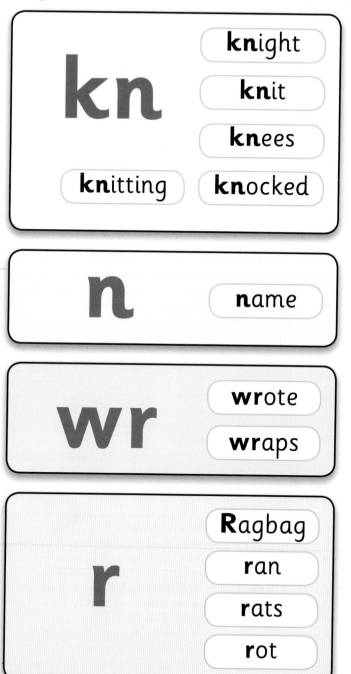

kn

- **kn**ight
- **kn**it
- **kn**ees
- **kn**itting
- **kn**ocked

n

- **n**ame

wr

- **wr**ote
- **wr**aps

r

- **R**agbag
- **r**an
- **r**ats
- **r**ot

"I wrote this play," said Wilma.
"I hope you like it."

Dad came onto the stage.
"I am a knight," he said.

Wilf came onto the stage.

"I am Sir Ragbag's page," he said.

Mum and Biff came on.

"I am Lady Ragbag," said Mum.

"I am the maid," said Biff.

"My name is Kate."

A giant came to the gate. Jake
was afraid.

Kate hid.

"Find a knight to fight me," cried the giant. "I will lay him out."

Kate ran to Sir Ragbag.

"The giant is on his way," she cried.

Sir Ragbag's face went pale. His knees knocked.

The giant came.

"I will fight the knight," he cried.

"No, I am a lady," said Sir Ragbag.
"The knight is not in today."

"What rot! You are a knight!" cried the giant. "I will fight you."

Jake had some tame rats. He let
them out.

"I hate rats," cried the giant.

He ran into Lady Ragbag's knitting.

"I was not afraid," said Sir Ragbag.

"That is the end," said Wilma.
"I hope you liked my play."

Talk about the story

Who wrote the play?

What did Sir Ragbag do?

Why did the giant try to run away?

What things are you afraid of?

Word jumble

Make the *kn, n, r,* and *wr* words from the story.

g a b r a g

a r n

s r t a

ing itt kn

m a n e

igh t kn

ck o kn ed

t o e wr

p s wr a

Spot the difference

Find the five differences between the two pictures of the knight.

Word search

Read these words. Can you find them all
in the grid?

ragbag

knees

write

rot

knocked

knight

not

ran

wraps

wrote

nap

v	r	a	g	b	a	g	n	i
a	w	r	i	t	e	t	o	k
j	x	k	n	i	g	h	t	w
q	w	r	a	p	s	n	c	h
r	o	t	r	d	x	n	a	p
o	k	n	e	e	s	h	j	p
q	w	r	o	t	e	o	p	q
t	i	k	n	o	c	k	e	d
r	r	n	o	t	w	r	a	n

Tips for reading *Uncle Max*

Children learn best when reading is relaxed and enjoyable.

- Talk about the title and the picture on page 29, and read the speech bubble.

- Find the following letter patterns in the story and talk about the sound they make when you read them: *le* as in *uncle*, *oi* as in *coin*, *ow* as in *down*, *ou* as in *cloud*, *er* as in *dinner*, *oe* as in *toe* and *o* as in *go*.

- Look at the *le, oi, er, ow, ou, oe* and *o* words on page 30. Say the sounds in each word and then say each word (e.g. *u-n-c-le, uncle; t-oe, toe; g-r-ou-n-d, ground*).

- Read the story together, then find the words with the letter patterns *le, oi, er, ow, ou, oe* and *o* in them.

- Talk about the story and do the fun activity at the end of the story.

Children enjoy re-reading stories and this helps to build their confidence.

Have fun!

After you have read the story, see how many different creatures you can find in the pictures.

The main sounds practised in this story are
'le' as in *uncle*, 'oi' as in *coin*, 'ou' as in *out* and *down*, 'er' as in *dinner*, 'oe' as in *toe* and *go*.

For more activities, free eBooks and practical advice to help your child progress with reading visit **oxfordowl.co.uk**

Uncle Max

It's fun when Uncle Max comes to stay!

Read these words.

unc**le**	d**ow**n
c**oi**n	**ou**t
cl**ou**d	n**oi**se
t**oe**	g**o**

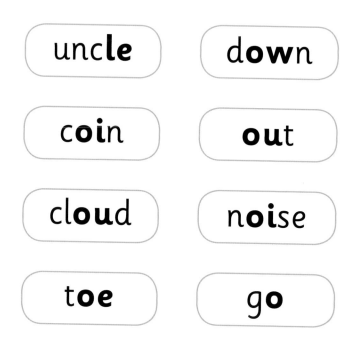

There was a noise outside the house.
An old car stopped with a bang and a
big cloud of smoke.

An odd-looking man got out. He had
white hair, a flowing blue cloak and
a big, green hat.

He's got odd shoes.

The man took out a huge case from the back of the car.

"Who is he?" asked Biff.

"He's my Uncle Max," said Dad.
"I have not seen him since I was a
little boy."

"I have been in Peru, and all over
the place," said Uncle Max, "but now
I'm back."

"Nice to meet you," Uncle Max said
to the children. "How do you do?"

"May I stay with you for a day or two?" went on Uncle Max. "I won't be a nuisance."

"Uncle Max has lots of cases," said Dad. "It may rain, so we need to get them inside."

Uncle Max had a parrot called Sue.

"She's quite shy," said Uncle Max.

"And she's quite rude," said Biff.

The children liked Uncle Max.
He showed them a trick. He made
a coin vanish.

"Look in your pockets," said Uncle Max. "See! Kipper has it."

Mum liked Uncle Max, too. He made
a big pot of stew for dinner.

"It's made of dragons' tails and goblins' toes," said Uncle Max.

Uncle Max had a tale to tell.

"Sit down and I will tell you about my escape from a snake," he said.

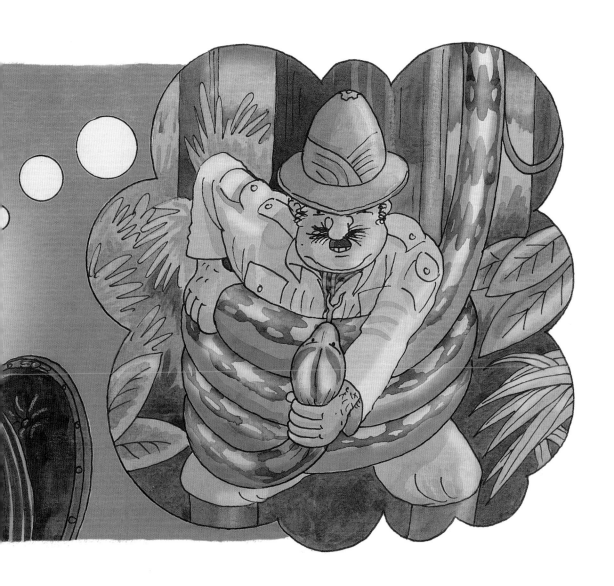

"I was in Peru when a giant snake
slid out of a tree. Its coils wound
round me," said Uncle Max.

"But I knew the song of the snake,

... so I sang to it in a deep voice ...

… the snake's coils unwound.

Then it lay on the ground and went to sleep."

"This is my ice cream machine," said Uncle Max.

"What kind of ice cream would you like? I can make red, pink, blue or green."

The ice cream machine began to
rattle and shake.

There was a flash and a bang.
The ice cream machine blew up.

"Look at my shed," said Dad.

"Er... do you fancy hot, black ice cream?" said Uncle Max.

"Time to go," said Uncle Max. "I will come and stay again, soon."

Talk about the story

When did Dad last see Uncle Max?

What story did Uncle Max tell about the snake?

What did Mum and Dad think when the shed blew up?

What stories do you like to tell?

A maze

Help Uncle Max find his parrot.

Stories for Wider Reading

Children learn best when reading is relaxed and enjoyable. These two stories use simple everyday language. You can help your child to read any more challenging words in the context of the story. Children enjoy re-reading stories and this helps to build their confidence and their vocabulary.

Tips for reading *Hungry Floppy*

- Talk about the title and the picture on page 59, and read the speech bubble.

- Share the story, encouraging your child to read as much of it as they can.

- Give lots of praise as your child reads, and help them when necessary.

- If your child gets stuck on a word that is easily decodable, encourage them to say the sounds and then blend them together to read the word. Read the whole sentence again. Focus on the meaning. If the word is not decodable, or is still too tricky, just read the word for them and move on.

- When you've finished reading the story, talk about it with your child, using the 'Talk about the story' questions at the end.

- Do the activity on page 86.

- Re-read the story later, again encouraging your child to read as much of it as they can.

Have fun!

This book includes these useful common words:
thought   very   so   away

For more activities, free eBooks and practical advice to help your child progress with reading visit **oxfordowl.co.uk**

Hungry Floppy

Hungry Floppy looks for food!

The family went camping. They put up a tent.

It took a long time to put up the tent. Floppy was hungry.

Floppy was so hungry, he ran off to look for food.

A man was cooking.

"That smells good," thought Floppy, "and I'm so hungry."

"Go away!" called the man.
"You can't have our dinner."
Floppy ran off.

Floppy saw a dog's bowl.

"This smells good," he thought, "and I'm so hungry."

A big dog barked at Floppy.
"Go away," growled the dog.
"You can't have my dinner."

Floppy was lost. He saw lots of tents but they all looked the same to him.

Floppy could smell something.
He sniffed and sniffed. Something
smelled good.

Floppy went inside the tent. He saw
three plates. There was a slice of cake
on each one.

By now, Floppy was *very* hungry. So he ate the big slice.

He was still hungry, so he ate the smaller slice.

But Floppy was still hungry, so
he ate the very small slice, too.
"I need a rest now," he thought.

There were three beds. Floppy lay on the blue bed, but it was too hard.

Then Floppy lay on the green bed,
but it was too soft.

In the end, he lay on the red bed.
It was not too hard or too soft. It was
just right. So he went to sleep.

Soon, a girl came back to the
tent with her mum and dad. It was
Anneena!

"Someone has eaten my cake,"
said Anneena.

"Someone has eaten *all* the cake," said Anneena's mum. "And look who's sleeping on your bed."

"It's Floppy!" said Anneena. "What are you doing here, you naughty dog?"

Anneena and her dad looked for Biff
and Chip. At last, they found them.

"What a surprise to see you!"
said Biff.

Anneena told them about Floppy.

"Never mind," said Dad. "Stay and
have some of our cake."

Talk about the story

Why did Floppy steal the food? Was he wrong to steal it?

Why didn't Floppy go and look for Biff and Chip himself?

How is this story like Goldilocks and the Three Bears?

What would you do if you got lost in a strange place?

Matching pairs

Find pairs of things that start with the same letter.
Which one isn't in the story?

Tips for reading *The Golden Touch*

Children learn best when reading is relaxed and enjoyable.

- Talk about the title and the picture on page 89, and read the speech bubble.

- Share the story, encouraging your child to read as much of it as they can with you.

- Give lots of praise as your child reads, and help them when necessary.

- If your child gets stuck on a word that is easily decodable, encourage them to say the sounds and then blend them together to read the word. Read the whole sentence again. Focus on the meaning. If the word is not decodable, or is still too tricky, just read the word for them and move on.

- When you've finished reading the story, talk about it with your child, using the 'Talk about the story' questions at the end.

- Do the activity on page 116.

- Re-read the story later, again encouraging your child to read as much of it as they can.

Have fun!

After you have read the story, find all the fruit hidden in the pictures.

This book includes these useful common words:
asked   children   chocolate   everything

For more activities, free eBooks and practical advice to help your child progress with reading visit **oxfordowl.co.uk**

The Golden Touch

What if everything turned into gold?

The children were dipping
strawberries into chocolate.

"They look yummy!" said Chip.

"They taste yummy!" said Kipper.

Kipper went to Biff's room. He
had chocolate on his hands. He got
chocolate on everything he touched.
"Go away, Kipper!" said Biff.

"You're getting chocolate on everything," said Chip.

"I wish everything I touched turned into chocolate," said Kipper.

"That's just greedy," said Chip.
Just then the magic key began to
glow. It took the children into an
adventure.

They saw a girl sitting by a river.

She was crying.

"What's the matter?" asked Biff.

"Come with me and I'll show you,"
said the girl. "My name is Zoe."
Zoe took them to a palace.

The children gasped. The palace
was made of gold, and a gold tree
stood outside.

Zoe took the children inside.
Everything was made of gold, even the
food on the table!

"My father is King Midas," said Zoe sadly. "He made a wish that everything he touched turned into gold. Now his wish has come true!"

"If the food turns into gold, how can he eat it?" asked Chip.

"He can't," said Zoe. "And if he touches me, I'll turn into gold too."

Just then King Midas came in. Zoe hid behind Biff. "My father used to hug me," she said, "but he mustn't do it anymore."

King Midas saw Floppy. "I love dogs,"
he said. "Come here!"

"Stop!" called Chip. "Don't touch that dog!"

It was too late. King Midas patted Floppy and turned Floppy into gold.

"I'm so sorry," said King Midas. "I forgot that everything I touch turns into gold. I wish I could turn him back into a real dog again."

"Who granted the wish?" asked Biff.

"It was Dionysus," said the king.

"Then we must go and see him," said Biff, "and ask him to help."

Dionysus lived on Mount Olympus.
It was a long way to walk, but at last
King Midas and the children arrived.

"Why have you come back to see me?" asked Dionysus.

"I have come to ask you to help me," said King Midas.

"I want everything back the way
it was," said King Midas. "My wish
was silly."

"You were foolish and greedy," said
Dionysus. "But you have learnt your
lesson. Now go back and do what
I tell you."

Dionysus told them to get water from the river. They had to pour it onto everything that had turned into gold.

"It works!" said King Midas.

"I'm so glad your dog is back."

"So am I!" said Kipper.

King Midas gave Zoe a hug. "What a fool I have been," he said. "I'm glad I can hug you now. I will never ask for gold again!"

King Midas looked at the children.
"Thank you for helping us," he said.

The key began to glow. It was time
to go home.

"Hey! Why did you do that?" asked Kipper, crossly.

"To stop you from turning into chocolate," laughed Chip.

Talk about the story

Why was
Zoe crying?

How was
Floppy turned
into gold?

Why was
King Midas's wish
foolish and greedy?

What would
you wish for?

Picture puzzle

Match each water carrier with his gold twin.

Remembering the stories together

Encourage your child to remember and retell the stories in this book.
You could ask questions like these:

- Who are the characters?
- What happens at the beginning?
- What happens next?

- How does the story end?
- What was your favourite part? Why?

Story prompts

When talking to your child about the stories, you could use these more
detailed reminders to help them remember the exact sequence of events.
Turn the statements below into questions, so that your child can give you the
answers. For example, *What is Wilma's play called? Who acts out
Wilma's play?* And so on …

The Knight Who Was Afraid

- Wilma writes her own play, *The Knight who was Afraid.*
- Everyone plays a different character.
- A giant wants to fight the knight, but Sir Ragbag is scared.
- Jake lets out some rats to distract the giant.

- The giant runs into Lady Ragbag's knitting.
- Sir Ragbag claims he isn't afraid, but no one believes him!

Uncle Max

- An odd-looking man gets out of the car. It's Uncle Max.
- Uncle Max asks if he can stay with them for a day or two.
- The children like him because he shows them tricks and tells stories.

- Uncle Max causes mischief and even blows up the shed making ice cream!

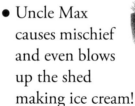

Hungry Floppy

- The family are trying to put up a tent.
- Floppy runs off to look for food.
- He tries to take lots of people's food and gets chased off by a dog.
- He gets lost, but finds some cake!
- Floppy goes to sleep on the red bed.

- Anneena finds Floppy and takes him back to Biff and Chip.

The Golden Touch

- Kipper gets chocolate on everything he touches.
- Kipper wishes that everything he touched turned into chocolate.
- The magic key takes the children to visit King Midas where everything is gold.
- His daughter, Zoe, is sad because her dad can't hug her anymore.

- The King turns Floppy into gold!
- Dionysus tells them to use river water to turn the gold things back to normal.

You could now encourage your child to create a 'story map' of each story, drawing and colouring all the key parts of them. This will help them to identify the main elements of the stories and learn to create their own stories.

Authors and illustrators

The Knight Who Was Afraid written by Roderick Hunt, illustrated by Nick Schon
Uncle Max written by Roderick Hunt, illustrated by Nick Schon
Hungry Floppy written by Roderick Hunt, illustrated by Alex Brychta
The Golden Touch written by Roderick Hunt, illustrated by Alex Brychta

OXFORD
UNIVERSITY PRESS

Great Clarendon Street, Oxford, OX2 6DP, United Kingdom

Oxford University Press is a department of the University
of Oxford. It furthers the University's objective of excellence
in research, scholarship, and education by publishing
worldwide. Oxford is a registered trade mark of Oxford
University Press in the UK and in certain other countries

Hungry Floppy, *The Knight Who Was Afraid*, *The Golden Touch*, *Uncle Max*
text © Roderick Hunt 2005, 2008, 2009

Hungry Floppy, *The Golden Touch* illustrations © Alex Brychta 2005, 2009
Uncle Max, *The Knight Who Was Afraid* illustrations © Alex Brychta and Nick Schon 2008

The characters in this work are the original creation of Roderick Hunt
and Alex Brychta who retain copyright in the characters

The moral rights of the authors have been asserted

Hungry Floppy first published in 2005
The Knight Who Was Afraid, *The Golden Touch* first published in 2008
Uncle Max first published in 2009

This Edition published in 2018

British Library Cataloguing in Publication Data
Data available

ISBN: 978-0-19-276425-6

10 9 8 7 6 5 4 3

Paper used in the production of this book is a natural, recyclable product
made from wood grown in sustainable forests. The manufacturing process
conforms to the environmental regulations of the country of origin.

Printed in China

Acknowledgements

Series Editors: Annemarie Young and Kate Ruttle